Puzzl

Deirdre Howard-Williams

For G.W.A.W.

PENGUIN ENGLISH

Pearson Education Limited
Edinburgh Gate, Harlow
Essex CM20 2JE, England
and Associated Companies throughout the world.

ISBN 0 582 45144 2

First published 2001
Copyright © Deirdre Howard-Williams 2001

Design and typesetting by Blue Pig Design Co
Illustrations by Martin Fish, Phil Healey, Ann Johns, Gillian Martin
Printed in Spain by Mateu Cromo S.A., Pinto, Madrid

Published by Pearson Education Limited in association with
Penguin Books Ltd, both companies being subsidiaries of Pearson plc.

CONTENTS

Introduction 5

1 Clothes word square .7

2 People 8

3 Question and answer 10

4 Opposites 1 12

5 Arms and legs, hands and fingers 14

6 How do they feel? 15

7 Jigsaw puzzle 16

8 Christina's family .18

9 Opposites 2 20

10 Journeys 21

11 Shopping at the supermarket 22

12 The kitchen clock 24

13 Making words 1 .25

14 Word families 1 .26

15 Find the different answer 1 27

16 Places in a town .28

17 What do you say? 30

18 Making words 2 .32

19 Living room word square 33

20 Opposites 3 34

21 How much and how many? 35

22 A-Z puzzle 36

23 Find the new words 38

CONTENTS

24 Find the letters *39*

25 Sam's birthday *40*

26 Find the different answer 2 .... *42*

27 Making words 3 .... *43*

28 Months and days *44*

29 Julia's room at university *46*

30 Beginnings and endings *48*

31 Word families 2 .... *49*

32 Picture puzzles *50*

Answers *52*

Word list *61*

INTRODUCTION

Puzzle Time

Puzzle Time is for students of English. There are four *Puzzle Time* books, and each book has a number of interesting word puzzles. These will help you learn English. Each *Puzzle Time* book uses words only from the Penguin Readers.

Puzzle Time 1

There are 32 puzzles in *Puzzle Time 1*. The words in these puzzles come from *Easystarts* and Levels 1 and 2 of the Penguin Readers. You can use this book in class or at home. There are answers to every puzzle at the back of the book. You can also find the important words from the puzzles at the back of the book.

***Puzzle Time* words**

Five words in *Puzzle Time 1* are not from Levels 1 and 2 of the Penguin Readers. These words are:

adjective   *Interesting, great, friendly* are *adjectives.*

verb   *To run, to talk, to like* are *verbs.*

puzzle   There are *puzzles* on nearly every page of *Puzzle Time 1*!

jigsaw   A *jigsaw* is a puzzle:

tick   ✓

New words

You have to learn a lot of words when you learn a language. These ideas will help you.

1   Write new words in a notebook. You can write a different word family (see puzzles 14 and 31) on each page. Write the English word and then write the same

word in your language next to it. Use each word in a short sentence:

dollar   *My new jacket cost fifty **dollars**.*

2   When you read a story or something in your English book, learn ten or fifteen important words from it. Then try to write the story again. Use the new words and other easy words.

3   Work with a friend. Write twenty or thirty new words. Put them into a box or an envelope. Take two words from the box and use them in a sentence. Then your friend takes two words and makes a sentence. Use every word from the box!

4   Learn some new words and write a puzzle with those words. Look at the puzzles in this book. Then give your puzzle to your friend. He or she writes the answers in the puzzle.

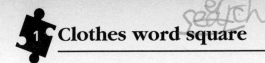

1 Clothes word square

Can you find eight names of clothes?

Do this: ⬭ ▶   or this: ⬭

Write the clothes here:

jacket   _shirts_   _Jeans_   _skirt_

coat   ....

F I M P Y S H P D H
C I W E A G M P E A
D O B J A C K E T T
R E H U K L N R S E
E Q U E S H I R T S
S T E V L W M G O J
S K I R T N O R T E
H I D K L I Y N V A
C O A T E L B I T N
P V T R O U S E R S

7

Write the names of these people.

1 This is my ...

2 This man brings you your food in a restaurant.

3

4 One man, two ...

5 You visit this person when you are ill.

6

7 The most important person at work

8 He or she studies at university.

9

10 person .... ?

11 Your mother and father are your ... .

¹D	A	U	G	H	T	E	R

Can you find another person in the puzzle? ....

9

Question and answer

Look at the questions below. Find answers on page 11, then write the conversations.

a doctor / I'm / a

b a / please / hamburger,

c seven o'clock / at

d is / yes, / it

e time / yes, / the / all

f thanks, / fine / you / and ?

g didn't / the / come / bus

h boss / new / your / I'm

i taxi / by

j town / the / centre / of / in

k grey / mine / the / is / horse

l little / a / yes,

1 _h   Who are you? I'm your new boss._

2 ....

3 ....

4 ....

5 ....

6 ....

7 ....

8 ....

9 ....

10 ....

11 ....

12 ....

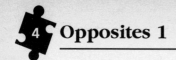

Opposites 1

Here are ten verbs. Find a verb in the box with
the opposite meaning to each verb and write them
below.

Verb	Opposite
1 start	*stop*
2 ask	
3 arrive	
4 hate	
5 begin	
6 buy	
7 learn	
8 pull	
9 open	
10 come	

atche	~~tspo~~	nwsrea
uhst	velea	ned
og	suhp	olev	lesl

Find a picture for one of the two verbs in 1-10 on page 12.
Write the number in the box.

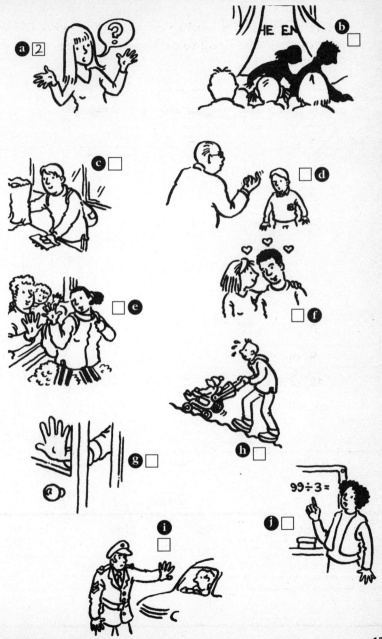

Arms and legs, hands and fingers

Look at the picture and write the words in the puzzle.

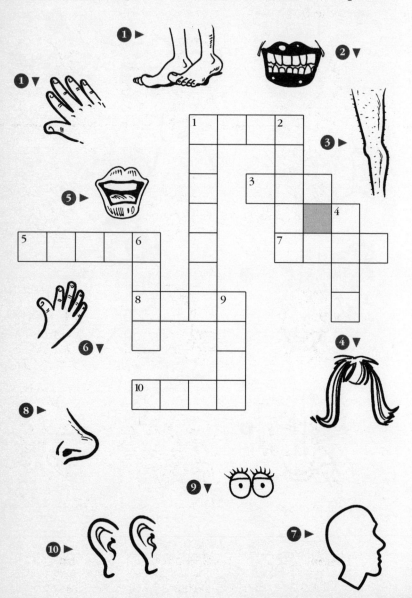

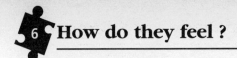

6 How do they feel ?

Look at the faces. How do they feel? Use the words in the box.

1 ..*fine*......   2 ....   3 ....

4 ....   5 ....   6 ....

7 ....   8 ....   9 ....

10 ....   11 ....   12 ....

| ~~fine~~ | angry | tired | excited | sad | hot | ill |
| cold | thirsty | bored | hungry | happy |

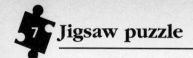

Jigsaw puzzle

Look at the pictures and write about them.

| DER IT. | BRIDGE A | THERE'S A BI | ND A CAT UN |

| CYCLE ON THE |

There's a bicycle on the

....

2

| CHILDREN | ARE PLAY | TLE IS | SEA AND THE |

| BEACH. | THE BOT | IN THE | ING ON THE |

....

....

3

IN FRO	E RADIO.	VISION AND THE	THE DO
NT OF THE TELE	BABY I	G IS SITTING	S NEXT TO TH

....

....

4

RE'S A TO	NORTH	AND	THE	WEST
IN THE SO	WN IN THE	A VILLAGE	UTH EAST.	

....

....

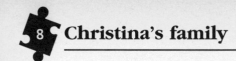

Christina's family

Here is a photo of Christina, her new baby and her family.

Look at this photo. This is my new baby son, Alex. My husband, Carlos, is next to me and my daughter Helena is standing next to him. My mother, Rosa, is wearing a big hat and talking to my father, Tony. My aunt Judy has got long hair and my uncle Peter is always laughing. My brother, Oliver, is eating a sandwich because he's always hungry and he's standing next to my pretty sister, Claire. My grandfather, Georgio, is very old so he's sitting down.

Who is Christina talking about? Write the name of each person on the photo.

Now write Christina's family in her family tree. These notes will help you:

Me = Christina
Write the oldest child on the left.
Christina's sister is older than her brother.
Christina's mother has got a sister.

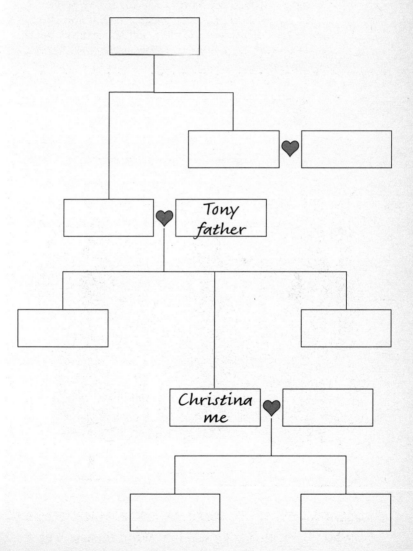

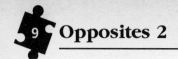

Opposites 2

Find the words with opposite meanings. Write one word from box A and one word from box B.

A

| ~~same~~ | out | never | yesterday | fast | after |
| back | first | future | early | best | down |

B

| slow | late | up | ~~different~~ | last | always |
| before | in | worst | front | tomorrow | past |

1 *same / different*

2 ....

3 ....

4 ....

5 ....

6 ....

7 ....

8 ....

9 ....

10 ....

11 ....

12 ....

Journeys

Find answers in the box. Look at the numbers on the left. Write that number of words.

6 People make journeys in this way on the ground.

...car...   ....

....

5 Verbs

....

....

4 You often take these things with you on a journey.

....

....

3 People make journeys in this way by sea or in the sky.

....

....

2 You can drive on this in a car.

....

1 There is one word in the box now. What is it?

....

> ticket walk train money bus boat street
> bicycle swim fly map foot drive ship road
> kilometre plane ~~car~~ taxi camera run

Shopping at the supermarket

Gerald has to buy a lot of things at the supermarket. Can you finish the words? The picture on page 23 will help you.

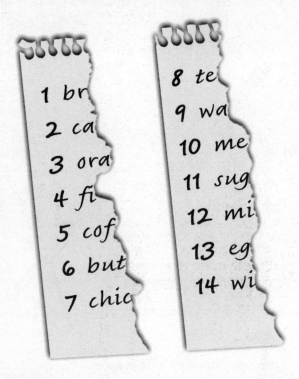

1 br
2 ca
3 ora
4 fi
5 cof
6 but
7 chic

8 te
9 wa
10 me
11 sug
12 mi
13 eg
14 wi

1 _bread_
2 ....
3 ....
4 ....
5 ....
6 ....
7 ....

8 ....
9 ....
10 ....
11 ....
12 ....
13 ....
14 ....

Gerald also bought something different.

What was it? ....

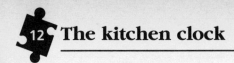

12 The kitchen clock

Look at the time on the kitchen clock and find the letters. Make words with the letters. The words are things in the kitchen.

1 quarter past eleven .....*knife* (FEK + IN).....

2 five past ten ....

3 twenty-five to two ....

4 four o'clock ....

5 quarter to five ....

6 half past eight ....

A lot of words in English are really two shorter words: *bed + room = bedroom*. Take one word from box A and one word from box B, and make ten longer words.

A

~~week~~   post   book   any   home   bath
     down   police   school   foot

B

thing   stairs   friend   card   work
woman   ~~end~~   room   shelf   ball

1 *weekend*
2
3
4
5
6
7
8
9
10

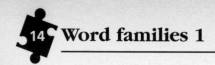

Put the words from the box into the right families.
There are four words in each family.

> ~~autumn~~   dollar   ~~dog~~   face   cook
> yellow   bank   spring   detective   horse
> summer   brown   pence   hair   green
> chicken   winter   pound   red   glasses
> doctor   waitress   cat   hat

Animals and birds
dog
....
....
....

Words about money
....
....
....
....

Times of the year
autumn
....
....
....

Colours
....
....
....
....

On the head
....
....
....
....

Jobs
....
....
....
....

One answer is different each time. Which answer is it?

1 Which is <u>not</u> cold?
  a ice-cream **b** snow **c** fire

2 Which is <u>not</u> big?
  a a card **b** a country **c** a city

3 Which is <u>not</u> blue?
  a the sea **b** the sky **c** the ground

4 Which is <u>not</u> usually young?
  a a baby **b** an aunt **c** a boy

5 Which is <u>not</u> wet?
  a rain **b** a shelf **c** a bath

6 Which is <u>not</u> a woman?
  a Sir **b** Mum **c** Madam

7 Which is <u>not</u> food?
  a a hamburger **b** an hour **c** breakfast

8 Which can you <u>not</u> listen to?
  a a photograph **b** a conversation **c** a song

9 Which is <u>not</u> dangerous?
  a a gun **b** a spoon **c** a knife

10 Which does <u>not</u> have two legs?
  a a cook **b** a bird **c** a fish

Write the names of these places in the puzzle on page 29. They are all places in a town.

1 A place with trees – children play here.

2 You go to this place when you are ill.

3

4 People can study here after they leave school.

5

6 You go here when you want to watch a film.

7 Children learn in this place and teachers teach them.

8

9 You can have a cup of coffee and talk to your friends in this place.

10 You can have dinner here.

11 You have to come here when you want to catch a plane.

12

13 There is a lot of money here!

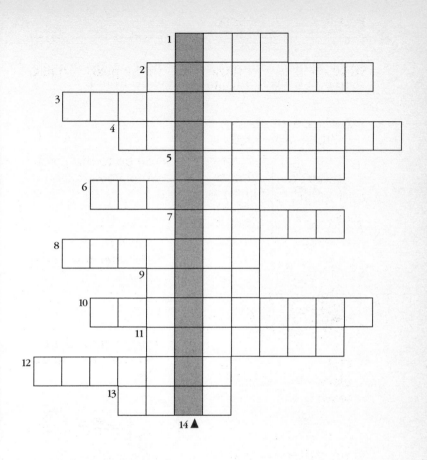

What is place number 14? ....

Who works there?

.... and ....

What do you say?

Look at the pictures. What are these people saying?
Use one word from A and one word from B.

A	B
Happy	you.
Goodbye	ninety!
I'm	~~me.~~
No,	careful!
~~Excuse~~	thanks.
It's	cake?
That's	birthday.
That's	right.
~~Yes,~~	Dad.
Thank	OK.
Some	~~Sir?~~
Be	sorry.

1

Excuse me.

Yes, Sir?

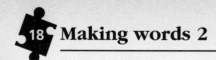

18 Making words 2

Make three longer words from each short word. Use the words below and the letters in each box.

1 EAR   *Dear* ....   *Wear* ....   *earLY* ....

2 SON   ....

3 IN   ....

4 OR   ....

ANGE	~~D~~	DO	FLO	G	LES
~~LY~~	PER	TH	TO	VITE	~~W~~

5 OUT   ....

6 AS   ....

7 WIN   ....

8 ALL   ....

B	C	DOW	E	IDE	LEEP
SE	SH	SIDE	SM	TER	WITH

Find the names of twelve different things in the living room.

Do this: ⬭ ▶ or this: ⬮ ▼

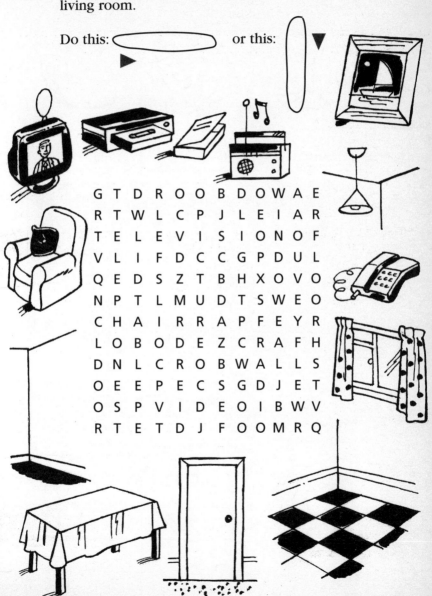

```
G T D R O O B D O W A E
R T W L C P J L E I A R
T E L E V I S I O N O F
V L I F D C C G P D U L
Q E D S Z T B H X O V O
N P T L M U D T S W E O
C H A I R R A P F E Y R
L O B O D E Z C R A F H
D N L C R O B W A L L S
O E E P E C S G D J E T
O S P V I D E O I B W V
R T E T D J F O O M R Q
```

33

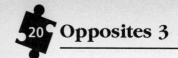

Look at the pictures. Which adjective goes with the picture?

1 (dirty) / clean

2 stupid / clever

3 pretty / ugly

4 weak / strong

5 sad / happy

6 big / small

7 cheap / expensive

8 easy / difficult

9 young / old

10 wet / dry

11 thin / thick

12 new / old

21 How much and how many?

How much or how many of these things do you want?
Find the right words.

coffee

water

a kilo of

a bottle of

a packet of

milk

a box of

wine

oranges

a glass of

cigarettes

a cup of

a litre of

chocolates

1 a litre of water   5 ....

2 ....   6 ....

3 ....   7 ....

4 ....

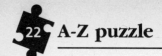

22 A-Z puzzle

Look at the picture and write the words in the puzzle.

1 How do you feel? **A** ⬜⬜⬜⬜⬜⬜

2 You can go to this place for a drink. **B** ⬜⬜⬜

3 You can smoke this. It's bad for you. **C** ⬜⬜⬜⬜⬜⬜⬜

4 **D** ⬜⬜⬜⬜⬜

5 **E** ⬜⬜⬜⬜

6 When everybody knows you, you are ... . (e.g. Madonna) **F** ⬜⬜⬜⬜⬜

7 **G** ⬜⬜⬜⬜

8 ½ **H** ⬜⬜⬜⬜

10 **9** **1** ⬜⬜⬜⬜⬜⬜⬜

J ⬜⬜⬜⬜⬜

11 You ... a football with your foot. **K** ⬜⬜⬜⬜

12 **L** ⬜⬜⬜⬜⬜

13 Twelve o'clock at night **M** ☐☐☐☐☐☐

14  **N** ☐☐☐☐☐☐☐

15 A lot of people work in this place. **O** ☐☐☐☐

16 **P** ☐☐☐☐☐

17 $\frac{1}{4}$ **Q** ☐☐☐☐☐

18 When you have a lot of money, you are ... . **R** ☐☐☐

19 **S** ☐☐☐

20 **T** ☐☐☐☐

21 **U** ☐

22 A very small town, with not many houses. **V** ☐☐☐☐☐

23 When a woman marries, she is a man's ... . **W** ☐☐☐

24 **Y** ☐☐☐

These people are in a restaurant. Find five more new verbs in their conversation. (Look **between** the words!)

1 Why don't you and John come and listen to music later?

2 Let's ask him when he arrives.

3 My new jeans were ready today.

4 That's good. They were only in the shop for ten days.

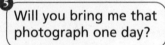

5 Will you bring me that photograph one day?

6 Of course, but I'm out each day this week. Next week?

1 ....   4 ....

2 ....   5 ....

3 ....   6 ....

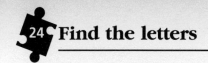

Find the letters

Finish the first word and start the next word with the same letter.

1 CLIM.*B*.RING

2 DI...NJOY

3 HIG...ERE

4 WH...NTO

5 PAG...ACH

6 HOU...EPEAT

7 LAUG...IT

8 WID...ND

9 ONL...EAR

10 ASLEE...LACE

11 ACROS...O

12 WOUL...ISCUSS

Finish the first word and start the next word with two letters. Here are the letters to help you:

TH	~~RE~~	LE	AR	AG	UN
AD	ON	ST	LE	OP	CH

13 MO.*RE*..ALLY

14 DE.....M

15 S.....DERSTAND

16 MIDD.....SSON

17 ST.....EN

18 TOO.....ERE

19 CHUR.....ANGE

20 SPO.....TO

21 FIR.....UDY

22 BRE.....DRESS

23 B.....AIN

24 POSSIB.....TTER

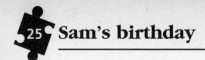

Sam's birthday

Sam wanted a lot of things for his birthday. Write the names of the things on the note on page 41.

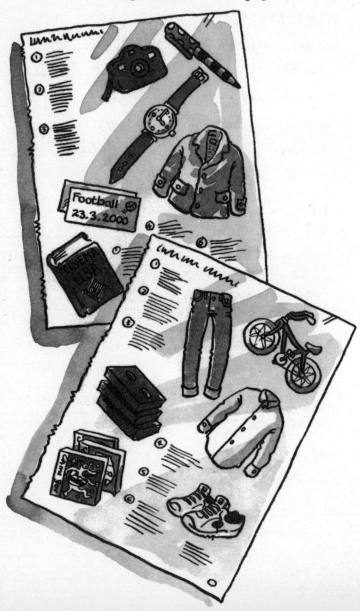

1 _ O O _ A _ O U _
   A _ E _ I _ A _ _ I _ _ _ _

2 _ A _ _ _ _

3 _ I _ _ E _ _ _ O _ _ _ _ E
   _ O O _ _ _ A _ _ _ _ A _ E

4 _ _ O _ _ _ _ _ _ O E _

5 _ E A _ _ _

6 _ _ _ I _ _

7 _ O _ _ U _ E R _ A _ E _

8 _ A _ _ E _

9 _ A _ E _ A

10 _ I _ E O _

11 _ E _

12 _ I _ _ _ _ _ E

1 *book about American films*

2 ....

3 ....

4 ....

5 ....

6 ....

7 ....

8 ....

9 ....

10 ....

11 ....

12 ....

26 Find the different answer 2

One answer is different each time. Which answer is it?

1 Which is <u>not</u> yellow?
   a the sun **b** the weather **c** butter

2 Which is <u>not</u> money?
   a a dollar **b** a litre **c** a pound

3 Which is <u>not</u> in the home?
   a a quarter **b** a cupboard **c** a toilet

4 Which is <u>not</u> a boy or a man?
   a an uncle **b** an aunt **c** a son

5 Which is <u>not</u> round?
   a a plate **b** a ball **c** a box

6 Which is <u>not</u> time?
   a changes **b** minutes **c** hours

7 Which is <u>not</u> dark?
   a midnight **b** night **c** midday

8 Which is <u>not</u> usually wood?
   a a table **b** a chair **c** a beach

9 Which is <u>not</u> white?
   a snow **b** milk **c** rain

10 Which <u>don't</u> you send?
   a a lesson **b** a postcard **c** a letter

27 Making words 3

A lot of words in English are really two shorter words:
sitting + room = sitting-room. Take one word from
box A and one word from box B, and make ten new
ideas.

A

| ~~ground~~ | first | telephone | wine | train |
| tennis | birthday | bus | car | city |

B

| number | party | ball | centre | glass |
| ~~floor~~ | name | stop | station | park |

1 *ground floor*

2 ....

3 ....

4 ....

5 ....

6 ....

7 ....

8 ....

9 ....

10 ....

357085
555763
701552
337331
245154
636119
563717

Months and days

Write months of the year or days of the week in the puzzle.

Across

3 On this day, people often go to parties in the evening because they can usually get up late the next day.

6 A cold month at the end of winter, before spring starts in March.

7 The month with the smallest number of letters in its name in English.

8 This day comes between Wednesday and Friday.

9 The month with the largest number of letters in its name in English.

10 The eleventh month of the year.

15 British schoolchildren have their summer holidays in this month.

16 The day with the largest number of letters in its name in English.

17 In Britain, flowers start to come out in this month. It is in spring.

Down

1 The first month of the year.

2 This month comes after May.

4 The last month of the year. Christmas Day is the 25th.

5 This month is often very windy in Britain. It comes before April.

6 This day comes before the weekend.

8 This day comes between Monday and Wednesday.

11 You go back to work after the weekend on this day.

12 People sometimes go to church on this day. They also get ready for work on the next day.

13 The tenth month of the year. It is in autumn.

14 This month is usually sunny and quite warm in Britain.

45

29 Julia's room at university

Julia is studying at university. You are a detective. Look at the picture of her room on page 47, read and tick (✔) **Yes** or **No**.

	Yes	No
1 Julia is tired.	✔	
2 She has got a cat.		
3 It's winter.		
4 It rained yesterday.		
5 She drives to university.		
6 She uses a computer.		
7 She likes going to the cinema.		
8 Julia will be very late for her ten o'clock class.		
9 She does not have many clothes.		
10 Julia can make coffee in her room.		
11 She is studying English.		
12 She wears glasses when she studies.		
13 She's got two radios.		
14 She has got long hair.		
15 Her sister is younger than she is.		
16 Julia likes wearing dresses.		
17 She likes reading in bed.		
18 She has got a new chair.		

Here are the beginnings of twelve sentences ... can you find the endings?

1 There was nothing $\boxed{e}$ **8** I like $\boxed{}$

2 Would you like $\boxed{}$ **9** Who's that man $\boxed{}$

3 Be careful, because these stairs $\boxed{}$

4 The film starts $\boxed{}$ **10** I know David $\boxed{}$

5 Why isn't $\boxed{}$ **11** Please give the books $\boxed{}$

6 Come as quickly $\boxed{}$ **12** I'm taller $\boxed{}$

7 We can't have lunch outside $\boxed{}$

a in the garden?

b watching television in the evenings.

c a drink?   **h** as you can.

d because it's raining.   **i** but I don't like him.

e in the box.   **j** in five minutes.

f are very dangerous.   **k** than my sister.

g Diane at work today?   **l** to the English teacher.

Put the words from the box into the word families.
there are three words in each family.

start	class	speak	future
bad	~~interesting~~	lesson	past	stop
homework	exciting	difficult	say
now	finish	funny	talk	boring

You use these
words when you
like something

...*interesting*......

....

....

You use these
words when you
don't like something

....

....

....

Words about
school

....

....

....

Words about time

....

....

....

Words for sounds

....

....

....

Words about
endings and
beginnings

....

....

....

49

Look at the pictures and find the names. Then write the names in front of the letters at the bottom of the page and make new words.

1 ..car........eful   6 ....ch

2 ....el   7 ....y

3 ....ly   8 ....ce

4 ....her   9 ....k

5 ....ise

10 ....fast
11 ....y
12 ....ly
13 ....d
14 ....nis
15 ....vite
16 ....terday
17 ....e
18 ....ch

ANSWERS

1 Clothes word square

```
F  I  M  P  Y  S  H  P  D  H
C  I  W  E  A  G  M  P  E  A
D  O  B  J  A  C  K  E  T  T
R  E  H  U  K  L  N  R  S  E
E  Q  U  E  S  H  I  R  T  S
S  T  E  V  L  W  M  G  O  J
S  K  I  R  T  N  O  R  T  E
H  I  D  K  L  I  Y  N  V  A
C  O  A  T  E  L  B  I  T  N
P  V  T  R  O  U  S  E  R  S
```

2 People

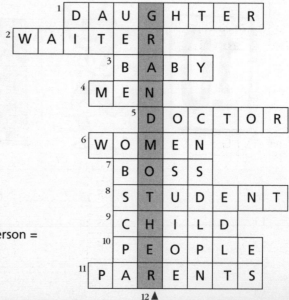

```
1  D  A  U  G  H  T  E  R
2  W  A  I  T  E  R
      3  B  A  B  Y
      4  M  E  N
         5  D  O  C  T  O  R
      6  W  O  M  E  N
         7  B  O  S  S
         8  S  T  U  D  E  N  T
         9  C  H  I  L  D
        10  P  E  O  P  L  E
     11  P  A  R  E  N  T  S
               12 ▲
```

The other person =
grandmother

52

3 Question and answer

2 b What would you like? A hamburger, please.
3 g Why are you late? The bus didn't come.
4 j Where do you live? In the centre of town.
5 c When does the film start? At seven o'clock.
6 k Which is yours? The grey horse is mine.
7 i How did you get to the airport? By taxi.
8 l Can you speak English? Yes, a little.
9 a What do you do? I'm a doctor.
10 f How are you? Fine thanks, and you?
11 d Is this your homework? Yes, it is.
12 e Do you use computers? Yes, all the time.

4 Opposites 1

2 answer 3 leave 4 love 5 end 6 sell 7 teach 8 push
9 shut 10 go

Pictures:
a 2 (ask) b 5 (end) c 6 (buy) d 10 (come) e 3 (leave)
f 4 (love) g 9 (open) h 8 (push) i 1 (stop) j 7 (teach)

5 Arms and legs, hands and fingers

6 How do they feel?

2 hungry **3** thirsty **4** angry **5** bored **6** excited **7** happy
8 sad **9** ill **10** hot **11** cold **12** tired

7 Jigsaw puzzle

1 There's a bicycle on the bridge and a cat under it.
2 The bottle is in the sea and the children are playing on the beach.
3 The dog is sitting in front of the television and the baby is next to the radio.
4 There's a town in the north west and a village in the south east.

8 Christina's family

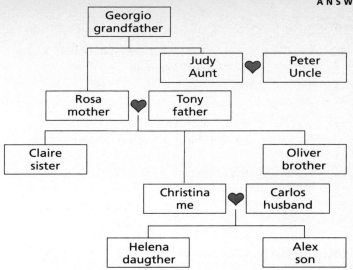

9 Opposites 2

2 out / in **3** never / always **4** yesterday / tomorrow
5 fast / slow **6** after / before **7** back / front **8** first / last
9 future / past **10** early / late **11** best / worst
12 down / up

10 Journeys

6 car, train, bus, bicycle, foot, taxi
5 walk, swim, fly, drive, run
4 ticket, money, map, camera
3 boat, ship, plane
2 street, road
1 kilometre

11 Shopping at the supermarket

2 cakes **3** oranges **4** fish **5** coffee **6** butter **7** chicken **8** tea
9 water **10** meat **11** sugar **12** milk **13** eggs
14 wine
Gerald also bought chocolate!

12 The kitchen clock

2 plate **3** spoon **4** glasses **5** cupboard **6** bottle

13 Making words 1

2 postcard   **3** bookshelf   **4** anything   **5** homework
6 bathroom   **7** downstairs   **8** policewoman
9 schoolfriend   **10** football

14 Word families 1

Animals: dog, horse, chicken, cat
Words about money: dollar, bank, pence, pound
Times of the year: autumn, spring, summer, winter
Colours: yellow, brown, green, red
On the head: face, hair, glasses, hat
Jobs: cook, detective, doctor, waitress

15 Find the different answer 1

1c   **2**a   **3**c   **4**b   **5**b   **6**a   **7**b   **8**a   **9**b   **10**c

16 Places in a town

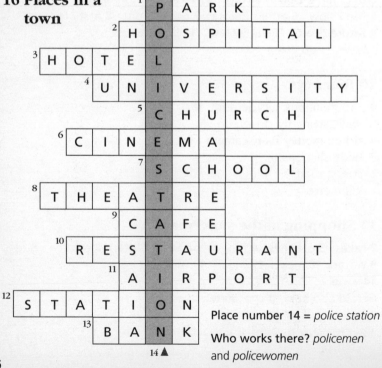

Place number 14 = *police station*

Who works there? *policemen* and *policewomen*

17 What do you say?

2 Happy birthday. / Thank you.
3 Some cake? / No, thanks.
4 Goodbye Dad. / Be careful.
5 It's ninety! / That's right.
6 I'm sorry. / That's OK.

18 Making words 2

2 song, lesson, person
3 thin, into, invite
4 orange, door, floor
5 shout, outside, without
6 ideas, asleep, seas
7 window, wine, winter
8 ball, call, small

19 Living room word square

20 Opposites 3

2 clever   **3** ugly   **4** strong   **5** happy   **6** big   **7** expensive
8 difficult   **9** young   **10** wet   **11** thick   **12** new

21 How much and how many?

2 a packet of cigarettes   **3** a box of chocolates   **4** a glass of milk
5 a bottle of wine   **6** a cup of coffee   **7** a kilo of oranges

22 A-Z puzzle

1 Afraid   **2** Bar   **3** Cigarette   **4** Dance   **5** East   **6** Famous   **7** Girl
8 Half   **9** Ice-cream   **10** Jump   **11** Kick   **12** Letter   **13** Midnight
14 Newspaper   **15** Office   **16** Picture   **17** Quarter   **18** Rich
19 Sky (or Sun)   **20** Throw   **21** Up   **22** Village   **23** Wife   **24** Year

23 Find the new words

2 hear   **3** answer   **4** end   **5** phone   **6** teach

24 Find the letters

2 diEnjoy   **3** higHere   **4** whOnto   **5** pagEach   **6** houRepeat
7 laugHit   **8** widEnd   **9** onlYear   **10** asleePlace   **11** acrosSo
12 woulDiscuss   **13** moREally   **14** deARm   **15** sUNderstand
16 middLEsson   **17** stOPen   **18** tooTHere   **19** churCHange
20 spoONto **21** firSTudy   **22** breADdress   **23** bAGain
24 possibLEtter

25 Sam's birthday

2 watch   **3** tickets for the football game   **4** sports shoes   **5** jeans
6 shirt   **7** computer games   **8** jacket   **9** camera   **10** videos
11 pen   **12** bicycle

26 Find the different answer 2

1 b   **2** b   **3** a   **4** b   **5** c   **6** a   **7** c   **8** c   **9** c   **10** a

27 Making words 3

2 first name   **3** telephone number   **4** wine glass   **5** train station
6 tennis ball   **7** birthday party   **8** bus stop (or bus station)
9 car park   **10** city centre

28 Months and days

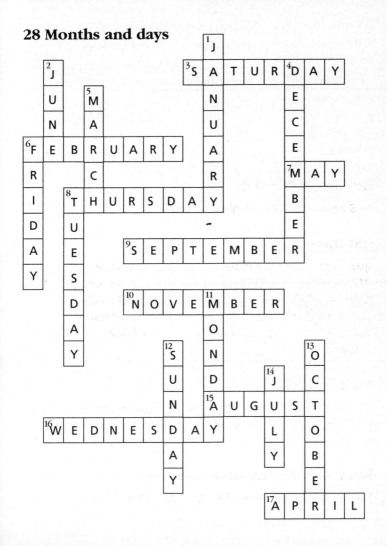

29 Julia's room at university

2 no **3** no **4** yes **5** no **6** yes **7** yes **8** yes **9** yes **10** yes
11 yes **12** yes **13** no **14** no **15** yes **16** no **17** yes **18** no

30 Beginnings and endings

2 c **3** f **4** j **5** g **6** h **7** d **8** b **9** a **10** i **11** l **12** k

31 Word families 2

You use these words when you like something: interesting, exciting, funny
You use these words when you don't like something: bad, difficult, boring
Words about school: class, lesson, homework
Words about time: future, past, now
Words for sounds: speak, say, talk
Words about endings and beginnings: start, stop, finish

32 Picture puzzles

2 hotel **3** early **4** father **5** noise **6** teach **7** many **8** pence
9 think **10** breakfast **11** busy **12** only **13** wind **14** tennis
15 invite **16** yesterday **17** hate **18** catch

These are the words from the answers and all the important words from the puzzles. The numbers after each word are the puzzle numbers.

across, 24
address, 24
afraid, 22
after, 9
again, 24
airport, 3, 16
always, 9
angry, 6
answer, 4, 23
anything, 13
April, 28
arm, 24
arrive, 4
ask, 4
asleep, 18, 24
August, 28
aunt, 8, 15, 26
autumn, 14
baby, 2, 7, 8, 15
back, 9
bad, 31
bag, 24
ball, 18, 26
bank, 14
bar, 22
bath, 15
bathroom, 13
beach, 7, 26
before, 9
begin, 4
best, 9
bicycle, 7, 10, 25

bird, 15
birthday party, 27
boat, 10
book, 25, 30
bookshelf, 13
bored, 6
boring, 31
boss, 2, 3
bottle, 7, 12, 21
box, 21, 26
boy, 15
bread, 24
breakfast, 15, 32
bridge, 7
bring, 24
brother, 8
brown, 14
bus, 3, 10
bus stop, 27
busy, 32
butter, 11, 26
buy, 4
café, 16
cake, 11
call, 18
camera, 10, 25
car, 10
card, 15
careful, 17, 30, 32
car park, 27
cat, 7, 14, 29
catch, 32

centre, 3
chair, 19, 26, 29
change, 24, 26
cheap, 20
chicken, 11, 14
child, 2
children, 7
chocolate, 11, 21
church, 16, 24
cigarette, 21, 22
cinema, 16, 29
city, 15
city centre, 27
class, 31
clean, 20
clever, 20
climb, 24
clothes, 29
coat, 1
coffee, 11, 21, 29
cold, 6
come, 4, 30
computer, 3, 29
computer game, 25
conversation, 15
cook, 14, 15
country, 15
cup, 21
cupboard, 12, 26
dance, 22
daughter, 2, 8
dear, 24

December, 28

detective, 14

die, 24

different, 9

difficult, 31

dirty, 20

discuss, 24

doctor, 2, 3, 14

dog, 7, 14

dollar, 14, 26

door, 18, 19

down, 9

downstairs, 13

dress, 1, 29

drive, 10

dry, 20

each, 24

ear, 5

early, 9, 32

east, 11

easy, 20

egg, 11

end, 4, 23, 24

enjoy, 24

excited, 6

exciting, 31

excuse me, 17

eye, 5

face, 14

famous, 22

fast, 9

father, 8, 32

February, 28

feet, 5

film, 3, 30

fine, 6

finish, 31

fire, 15

first, 11, 15

first name, 27

fish, 11, 15

floor, 18, 19

fly, 10

foot, 10

football, 13, 25

Friday, 28

front, 9

funny, 31

future, 9, 31

game, 25

girl, 22

glass, 12, 21

glasses, 14, 29

go, 4

goodbye, 17

grandfather, 8

grandmother, 2

green, 14

grey, 3

ground, 15, 27

ground floor, 27

gun, 15

hair, 5, 14, 29

half, 22

hamburger, 3, 15

hand, 5

happy, 6

happy birthday, 17

hat, 1, 14

hate, 4, 32

head, 5

hear, 23

here, 24

high, 24

hit, 24

homework, 3, 13, 31

horse, 3, 14

hospital, 16

hot, 6

hotel, 16, 32

hour, 15, 24, 26

how, 3

hungry, 6

husband, 8

ice-cream, 15, 22

idea, 18

ill, 6

in, 7, 9

in front of, 7

interesting, 31

into, 18

invite, 18, 32

jacket, 1, 25

January, 28

jeans, 1, 25

July, 28

jump, 22

June, 28

kick, 22

kilo, 21

kilometre, 10

knife, 12, 15

know, 30

last, 9

late, 3, 9, 29

laugh, 24

learn, 4

leave, 4

leg, 5

lesson, 18, 24, 26, 31

letter, 22, 24, 26

light, 19

like, 3, 30

litre, 3, 21, 26

live, 3

long, 29

love, 4

lunch, 30

madam, 15

many, 32

map, 10

March, 28

May, 28

mean, 23

meat, 11

men, 2

midday, 26

middle, 24

midnight, 22, 26

milk, 11, 21, 26

minute, 26

Monday, 28

money, 10

more, 24

mother, 8

mouth, 5

mum, 15

never, 9

newspaper, 22

next to, 7

next, 23

night, 26

noise, 29, 32

north-west, 7

nose, 5

nothing, 30

November, 28

now, 31

October, 28

office, 22

OK, 17

old, 20

only, 24, 32

onto, 24

open, 4, 24

orange, 11, 18, 21

out, 9

outside, 18, 30

packet, 21

page, 24

parents, 2

park, 16

past, 9, 31

pen, 25

pence, 14, 32

people, 2

person, 18

phone, 23

photograph, 15

picture, 19, 22

place, 24

plane, 10

plate, 12, 26

play, 7

policeman, 16

policewoman, 13, 16

police station, 16

possible, 24

postcard, 13, 26

pound, 14, 26

pretty, 20

pull, 4

push, 4

quarter, 22, 26

quickly, 30

radio, 7, 19, 29

rain, 15, 26, 29

really, 24

red, 14

repeat, 24

restaurant, 16

rich, 22

road, 10

run, 10

sad, 20

same, 8

Saturday, 28

say, 31

school, 16

schoolfriend, 13

sea, 7, 15, 18

sell, 4

September, 28

shelf, 15

ship, 10

shirt, 1, 25

shoes, 25

shout, 18

shut, 4

sir, 15

sister, 8, 29

sit, 7

skirt, 1

sky, 15, 22

slow, 9

small, 18, 20

snow, 15, 26
so, 24
son, 8, 18, 26
song, 15, 18
sorry, 17
south-east, 7
speak, 3, 31
spoon, 12, 15, 24
sports shoes, 25
spring, 14
stairs, 30
start, 3, 4, 30, 31
stop, 4, 24, 31
street, 10
student, 2
study, 24, 29
stupid, 20
sugar, 11
summer, 14
sun, 24, 26
Sunday, 28
swim, 10
table, 19, 26
talk, 31
tall, 30
taxi, 3, 10
tea, 11
teach, 4, 23, 32
teeth, 5
telephone, 19
telephone number, 27
television, 7, 19
tennis, 32
tennis ball, 27

thank you, 17
thanks, 17
theatre, 16
there, 24
thin, 18, 20
think, 32
thirsty, 6
throw, 22
Thursday, 28
ticket, 10, 25
time, 3
tired, 6, 29
toilet, 26
tomorrow, 9
tooth, 24
town, 3, 7
train, 10
train station, 27
trousers, 1
Tuesday, 28
uncle, 7, 26
under, 7
understand, 24
university, 16
up, 9, 22
use, 3
video, 19, 25
village, 7, 22
waiter, 2
waitress, 14
walk, 10
wall, 19
watch, 25
water, 11, 21

weak, 20
wear, 29
weather, 26
Wednesday, 28
weekend, 13
what, 3
when, 3
where, 3
which, 3
who, 3, 24
why, 3
wide, 24
wife, 22
wind, 32
window, 18, 19
wine, 11, 18, 21
wine glass, 27
winter, 14, 18, 29
without, 18
women, 2
worst, 9
would, 3, 24
year, 22, 24
yellow, 14
yesterday, 9, 32
younger, 29